Dear Parents

As we all know, from an early age, the information our children learn about religion will later influence their beliefs, attitudes, and behaviors in later years.

This series tells about the birth, infancy, and childhood of Prophet Muhammad (peace and blessings be upon him), with stories and drawings that will appeal to our children and help them to understand.

We hope and believe that you and your children will enjoy this series and find the stories not only entertaining, but informative as well.

2

THE CHILD WHO LIT UP THE DESERT

The first rays of the Sun woke up two camels living in Mecca. The brown camel said to her friend: "Do you know something?
I feel so happy. I am very excited about the journey we are making today."
The grey camel said "Of course! Who wouldn't feel excited about making a journey with the most beautiful of all children, the Child of Light?"
Amina, the Child of Light's mother, and his nanny, Umm Ayman, had woken up as well. Like the camels, they were excited about this trip. All the preparations were complete and they were ready to start their journey to Medina.

4

The two camels were so happy on this journey with the Child of Light that they didn't notice how the time had passed. It was nearly evening now. The brown camel knelt down by the side of the road to rest. A little bit later her friend, the grey camel, came up and rested next to her. "Hey, do you see that" said the grey camel. "Look how the Child of Light is watching the stars and the Moon!" The brown camel answered him: "Yes, I can see him. He is a child that takes in everything around him. Even though he is only five years old, he is very smart and thinks a lot." After chatting a bit more, the two camels dropped off into a deep sleep. They woke up at first light and continued their journey. Finally they reached Medina. They first visited the grave of Abdullah, the Child of Light's father. They then went to his uncle's place to stay with him and his family.

6

The next day, as the camels basked in the sun in front of the house, they kept one eye on its door. Just then the Child of Light and his nanny came outside. The camels were very pleased. As the Child of Light and his nanny were sitting outside the house, two men crossed over in front of them. They couldn't take their eyes off the Child of Light. Their stares seemed to make the Child of Light uncomfortable, and he went back inside the house. The camels, upon noticing this, went a little closer to the two men. They were wondering what the men were talking about. They quietly began to listen.

8

The two men went up to
Umm Ayman and asked:
"What is the name of that child?"
"Why do you ask?"
Umm Ayman replied.
"That child has a beautiful face, and
he resembles a child about whom
we have been given some
information...we were
just wondering..."
The Child of Light's nanny
answered them:
"His name is Muhammad."
"Does he not have any other name?
"Yes, he does. He is also called
Ahmad."
The two men smiled at one
another. It seemed as if they had
found who they had been
looking for.
They pleaded with Umm Ayman:
"Please, could you call him outside
for a few minutes?"
The camels looked at one another.
They couldn't make head or tail of
what the two men were talking
about. Why did they want to see
the child so much? The two camels
were truly puzzled.

9

The two men explained themselves to the nanny: "Our intentions are good. And we love him in the name of Allah."
The nanny, understanding that the two men had only good intentions, went inside to get the Child of Light. The grey camel was unable to contain his excitement.
"Oh, look there! Look at the men bowing down to the ground in front of the Child of Light. Their eyes are full of wonder."
The brown camel said: "Look, how carefully they are looking at him."
Just then, the two men began to talk among themselves. The taller of the two said: "I think that this child is the one that I have read about in my books. He is the final prophet. His name is Ahmad. This is a sign."

The other man said:
"Well, then, we should find the
mark of prophethood on his
back. We need to look
at his back."
The grey and brown camels
overheard this conversation.
Their hearts began to beat with
excitement. Their eyes opened
wide as they silently followed
the two men.

13

14

The grey camel said to his friend: "Look there, look!" He nodded toward the men who started to examine the back of the Child of Light.
Dear Allah, how wide their eyes became with astonishment! It was clear that they were very excited. On the boy's back was the mark of prophethood, and upon this confirmation, the men began to shout with excitement: "Here he is, this beautiful child is the last prophet for humanity. He is the most valuable person." And then they continued on their way, talking excitedly.
The camels couldn't hide the emotions they felt after all that they had seen. They began to cry with joy.

15

Umm Ayman, the nanny of the Child of Light, had also heard what the men had confirmed Her face showed how pleased she was.

The two camels were so happy that they couldn't keep still. The grey camel looked at the his friend and together they gave thanks:

"It has always been clear that Muhammad was different. Allah, thank you so much for showing him to us and for allowing us to serve him."

The two camels would never forget this trip to Medina.

16

Questions to think about:

1. Why were the two camels so excited?
2. Why did the Child of Light visit Medina with his mother and nanny?
3. Why did the two strangers want to see the Child of Light?

Awaiting the Prophet

Hello there.
We are two camels, and we are
very good friends.
We are so excited right now.
Do you want to know why? We are about to
set off on a journey with the Child of Light
and his mother Amina to Medina.
We both wonder what will happen on this
journey.
Where will we stay in Medina?
What will the two strangers do when they see
the Child of Light?
Are you curious too? Well then, come and
join us on our journey.

Awaiting the Prophet Series

THE LIGHT CHILDREN's
www.thelightpublishing.com

ISBN 978-1-59784-108-5

9 781597 841085